This book is dedicated with
love to my granddaughters
Madeleine and Claire.
May you always wonder.

If we wonder often, the gift
of knowledge will come.

-Native American Proverb

www.mascotbooks.com

From My Window I See... The Seasons

For more information, please contact:
Mascot Books
620 Herndon Parkway #320
Herndon, VA 20170
info@mascotbooks.com

Library of Congress Control Number: 2018914078

CPSIA Code: PRT0719A
ISBN-13: 978-1-64307-197-8

Printed in the United States

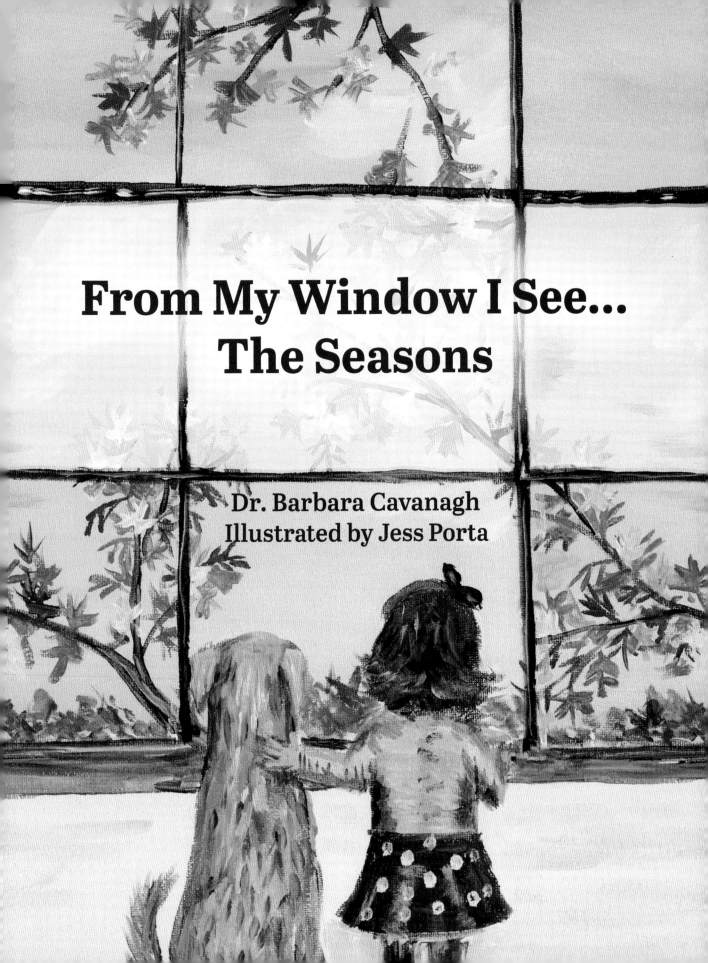

From My Window I See...
The Seasons

Dr. Barbara Cavanagh
Illustrated by Jess Porta

All through the year
from my window I see,
the world outside
looking back at me.

Just like the water
keeps turning the old
mill's wheel,

Every year turns into
four seasons that I
can see and feel.

I can see from my
window the changes
each season,

But I wish I
understood some
of the reasons...

Why do green leaves
in Summer change
colors in the Fall?

Why in Winter do
trees have branches,
but no leaves at all?

From my window I see, each Fall that the birds fly away.

Yet in Summer the birds fly from tree to tree all day.

I guess that's why seasons each have a name,

So that we will know they will not be the same.

I think I like Fall more than the rest.

From my window I see, Fall's colors are best.

In Fall I see children playing in leaves on the ground.

There is a chill in the air, Winter soon comes around.

From my window I see,
Winter's white snow

And children in coats
wherever they go.

In Winter from my window sparkling icicles I see,

But I know they are just frozen water on a tree.

Or maybe it's springtime that I like the most to see.

New fruit on the trees looks delicious to me.

When I rise in the Spring I can see new trees and flowers.

It makes me want to stay at my window for hours.

But Summer is really the best season that can be.

Outside children are fishing and swimming, I see.

From the Summer sun,
much heat is made,

And in Summer's heat,
animals rest in the shade.

From my window I see,
one season is not best of all.

I cannot choose one:
Winter, Spring, Summer, or Fall.

ABOUT THE AUTHOR

Dr. Barbara Cavanagh, teacher, psychologist, and author, has spent her life with children. For 30 years, she was a psychologist with the pediatric practice founded by Dr. Lawrence C. Pakula, who taught her to find the very best within every child. The From My Window series of books was developed to promote finding and building the best in children by improving developmental skills and strengthening relationships through reading in a way that time spent in front of a screen cannot do.

Dr. Cavanagh is a wife, mother, and grandmother who lives in Bethesda, Maryland, near the heroines of this book, with her husband of 40 years.

ABOUT THE ILLUSTRATOR

Jess Porta is a children's book author and illustrator who lives in Raleigh, North Carolina, with her husband. Jess has a background in human rights and in addition to collaborative projects like this one, Jess has her own series of children's books that address social issues. Jess is also the Director of HQ Raleigh, an entrepreneurial community in North Carolina.